Bits of Colorado

Bits of Colorado

Helen Hunt Jackson's Writings for Young Readers

Edited by Mark I. West

For my son,
Gavin Northcott West

Cover photo: Helen Hunt Jackson, c. 1865
Courtesy Colorado Springs Pioneers Museum

Photo page 8: Mrs. Maxwell. Courtesy, Colorado Historical
Society F-33, 373

Publisher's Note: The articles in *Bits of Colorado—Helen Hunt Jackson's Writings for Young People* are published with original spelling and punctuation.

FILTER PRESS, LLC
Palmer Lake, CO

ISBN: 0-86541-056-9
Library of Congress Card Number: 00-191172

Contents

From *The Crest of the Continent*, (Chicago: R.R Donnelley and Sons, 1885).

NORTH CHEYENNE CAÑON.

Acknowledgments

This book grew out of an extensive research project on Helen Hunt Jackson's Colorado writings, which was supported in part by funds provided by The University of North Carolina at Charlotte. Throughout this project, I received valuable support and assistance from the staff of the Colorado Springs Pioneers Museum.

Two people helped me prepare the final manuscript—Sharon Green and Kawana Howard. My appreciation goes to both of them.

Finally, my thanks go to my wife, Nancy Northcott, and my son, Gavin West. I could not ask for a more supportive family.

About the Editor

A native of Colorado, Mark I. West is now a professor of English at the University of North Carolina at Charlotte. He teaches courses in children's literature and serves as coordinator of the American Studies Program. He has written or edited ten books, including *Westward to a High Mountain: The Colorado Writings of Helen Hunt Jackson,* which was published by the Colorado Historical Society in 1994.

Foreword

The literary works of Helen Hunt Jackson have retained a particular fascination for modern readers even now, over a hundred years after her death in 1885. Although she was best known for her novel, *Ramona*, and her advocacy of Native American rights, Jackson also wrote poetry and produced occasional short stories and essays for children—perhaps as a way of dealing with the untimely deaths of her own two sons. In assembling this collection of "Writings for Young Readers" from Helen Hunt Jackson's out-of-print books and several nineteenth-century children's magazines, Professor Mark West has produced a volume that will give Jackson fans considerable pleasure.

The six works contained herein, while originally written for the youth of Helen Hunt Jackson's time, will perhaps be of more interest today to grownups. Their style reflects the Victorian attitude towards children, who were generally regarded as little adults. Four of the pieces are descriptive essays about life in Helen Hunt Jackson's adopted Colorado, for which she was a tireless promoter. Colorado, having only attained statehood in 1876, was still very much a frontier at the time of the writing, and these essays were probably read with great interest in the East. Two creative works are included: a charming poem called "Colorado Snow-Birds," and a short story, "The Ants' Monday Dinner," which has a certain gruesome appeal.

The Pioneers Museum of Colorado Springs has a special tie with Helen Hunt Jackson. A native of New England, she moved west for her health in her early 40s and made this city her home for the remainder of her life. The house where she lived with her husband, William Sharpless Jackson, was torn down in 1961, but three complete rooms—the living room, dining room, and Helen Hunt Jackson's study, where she wrote—were saved and reassembled in the Pioneers Museum. All were preserved in their original condition, complete with furnishings, and are on display for the public to enjoy.

William C. Holmes, Director
Colorado Springs Pioneers Museum

From *The Crest of the Continent* 1885.

CHEYENNE FALLS.

Bits of Colorado

Introduction

Helen Hunt Jackson often wrote about her adopted state of Colorado. In 1878, she published a selection of her Colorado writings in a book titled *Bits of Travel at Home*. A reviewer for the *Hartford Courant* praised this book and its author. "She is a fervent apostle of her new home," the reviewer wrote, "and if any body can convince the East that it is a Paradise to live in, and cause a rush of settlers to it, it is the author of this volume. Next to the lodestone of its mineral wealth, we verily believe that Colorado owes a chief debt for its good reputation to its best known and most distinguished citizen." This reviewer may have been exaggerating a little, but Jackson certainly ranked among Colorado's foremost authors during the nineteenth century.

In *Bits of Travel at Home*, Jackson collected eighteen Colorado travel sketches that had originally appeared in various Eastern magazines, such as *Atlantic Monthly*, the *New York Independent*, and *Scribner's Monthly*. The selections in *Bits of Travel at Home* were for adult readers, but she also wrote a number of short Colorado pieces that she intended for children, although these were not reprinted in *Bits of Travel at Home*. A few years earlier she had included two selections about Colorado in her book *Bits of Talk, in Verse and Prose, for Young Folks* (1876). Her other Colorado writings for children, however, were never reprinted in a book until now.

Bits of Colorado: Helen Hunt Jackson's Writings for Young Readers consists of six selections. "A Colorado Woman's Museum" originally ran as an article in the famous children's magazine *St. Nicholas*, which was edited by Jackson's friend Mary Mapes Dodge. "Ranch Life in Colorado," "Health Resorts in Colorado," and "Health-Seeking in Colorado" all initially appeared in the *Youth's Companion*. Jackson's fanciful natural history essay "The Ants' Monday Dinner" appeared as a chapter in *Bits of Talk*. The last selection, a poem titled "Colorado Snow-Birds," first ran in *St. Nicholas* in 1875 and was reprinted the next year in *Bits of Talk*.

Written in the late 1870s or early 1880s, these selections provide modern-day readers with vivid glimpses into Colorado's early years. Jackson filled these writings with descriptions of places unique to Colorado, such as Boulder Canyon, Ute Pass, her hometown of Colorado Springs, and Martha Maxwell's Rocky Mountain Museum. In some of these selections, she explained the appeal of Colorado to ranchers, health-seekers, adventurers, and naturalists. In other selections, she discussed Colorado's wildlife and pondered the relationship between these animals and the state's human residents. Since Jackson was writing about her own experiences and observations, there is a freshness and immediacy to these pieces that is often missing in more recent works about Colorado history.

Although Jackson came to be known as one of Colorado's most prominent supporters, she did not especially like the place when she first saw it. Her introduction to Colorado came in 1873 when she reluctantly agreed to spend the winter in Colorado Springs after her physician suggested that the town's high altitude and low humidity might help cure her respiratory problems. She longed for better health, but the idea of leaving her home in New England and moving to a frontier town did not sound too appealing to her.

At this point in her life, she was in her mid-forties and had already experienced much emotional upheaval. Her first husband, Edward Bisell Hunt, had died in an accident ten years earlier. Her two sons had also died, one in infancy and the other at the age of nine. Given all the stress she had already endured, she did not want to take on the added stress of moving across the country. Furthermore, she felt quite at home in her native New England. She liked the historic quality of New England's towns, and she had many friends scattered around the region. If it were not for New England's damp winters, she would likely have ignored her doctor's advice. Ultimately, however, the attraction of escaping to a better climate convinced her to give Colorado Springs a try.

Traveling by train, she set out for Colorado in November 1873. When the train entered the Colorado Territory, she looked out her window and saw the vast flat land of the Great Plains. The sight left her cold. She described it as a "blank, bald, pitiless gray, under a gray November sky." Her initial reactions to Colorado Springs were also negative. Since the town was only three years old at the time, the buildings were so new that they looked raw to her. She wanted to turn around and go back to New England, but she had promised her doctor that she would stay for at least a month. She moved into the Colorado Springs Hotel, and before long her feelings toward Colorado started to change.

Just as her doctor had predicted, Colorado's climate agreed with her. Her health improved dramatically, and she soon felt well enough to take day trips around the area. She enjoyed exploring the nearby mountains and visiting the ranches and mining towns that surrounded Colorado

Springs. She also enjoyed meeting the colorful assortment of people who had moved into the area.

One of the people with whom she became friends was a banker named William Sharpless Jackson. Since both of them stayed at the Colorado Springs Hotel, they frequently saw each other. As their friendship deepened, he began taking some of his afternoons off so that he could accompany her on her buggy rides through the countryside. One day he proposed to her. She was not sure she wanted to remarry, but she gradually warmed to the idea. On October 22, 1875, they were married, and not long afterwards they moved into an elegant Victorian house in the center of Colorado Springs. This home remained her primary residence until her death in 1885.

Although she had achieved some success as a poet before moving to Colorado, Jackson's writing career blossomed after she moved to the West. Fifteen of the seventeen books that she published during her lifetime came out while she was living in Colorado, including her two most famous books: *A Century of Dishonor: A Sketch of the United States Government's Dealings with Some of the Indian Tribes*, a nonfiction work published in 1881, and *Ramona*, a novel published in 1884.

Jackson also had considerable success as a children's author. Her most important children's book, *Nelly's Silver Mine: A Story of Colorado Life*, was published in 1878. One of the first children's novels set in Colorado, *Nelly's Silver Mine* tells the story of a family that moves from Massachusetts to Colorado for the sake of the father's health. The book contains vivid descriptions of Colorado's mountains, canyons, and rock formations, as well as its distinctive plants and animals. When writing this book,

Jackson drew heavily on her experiences and observations during her frequent excursions around the state. These same excursions served as the basis for some of her shorter writings for children.

"A Colorado Woman's Museum" grew out of a trip she took to Boulder to see Martha Maxwell's Rocky Mountain Museum. Like Jackson, Maxwell was an educated and independent woman who felt drawn to Colorado. An avid naturalist and skilled taxidermist, Maxwell set out to create a museum that would exhibit specimens of some of the animals native to the Rocky Mountains. When building her displays, she attempted to re-create the animals' natural habitats. She also tried to place the animals in groupings that corresponded with the animal groupings that would be found in nature. At the time, this was a revolutionary approach to displaying animal specimens, and it helped attract attention to her museum when it opened in 1874. Jackson visited Maxwell's museum in 1875 and wrote two articles about her impressions of it, one for adults and one for children. In the beginning of "A Colorado Woman's Museum," Jackson took a fairly light-hearted approach to describing the museum, but she closed the article by encouraging children to rethink their attitudes toward animals.

"Ranch Life in Colorado" grew out of the research she did for *Nelly's Silver Mine*. Since the characters in this book eventually move to a ranch, Jackson visited numerous ranches to make sure that she could write accurately about the details of ranch life. In this article, she described three types of ranches: cattle ranches, sheep ranches, and farm ranches.

In both "Health Resorts in Colorado" and "Health-Seeking in Colorado," Jackson drew on her own experiences at the various places in Colorado that were supposed to possess curative powers. When she first moved to Colorado she visited several health resorts in an effort to regain her strength and vitality.

Jackson devoted most of "Health Resorts in Colorado" to describing three of the state's most popular health resorts: Manitou Springs, Canon City, and Idaho Springs. She ended this article, however, with an interesting comparison of Colorado Springs and Denver. Although she attempted to be even-handed in her accounts of these two communities, she did not succeed in hiding her preference for Colorado Springs.

In "Health-Seeking in Colorado," Jackson tried to explain why so many people moved to Colorado to improve their health. Since she knew numerous such people, she was able to make some keen observations about the experiences that these people had when they relocated to Colorado. She focused on how Colorado's climate affected the health of these people, but she also commented on how these transplanted Easterners coped with Colorado's frontier lifestyle.

Jackson trained her observant eye on animals as well as people. She enjoyed watching the behavior of animals, and she often wrote about them. In fact, she published three children's books about cats. When writing about animals, Jackson often combined accurate descriptions of their activities with imaginative interpretations about the significance of their behavior.

Her interest in the lives of other creatures can be seen in her essay "The Ants' Monday Dinner." She based this essay on an experience she had while sitting on a Colorado hillside one afternoon. As she recounted in her essay, she had noticed an ant carrying a caterpillar and had decided to see where the ant was taking its still struggling prey. In her essay, she provided a detailed description of the ant's difficult trip back to its colony. She also, however, included amusing dialogue, which she imagined the ant might have said or thought.

Jackson's poem "Colorado Snow-Birds" stemmed from her observations of the birds that often appeared near her home after a snowstorm. She began her poem by describing these birds and their behavior, but she closed it on a spiritual note. The snow-birds, she suggested, are able to find "grains" on seemingly "barren plains" by putting their trust in "the Father in the skies."

For Jackson, nature was a constant source of spiritual inspiration. On Sundays, for example, she often visited nearby Cheyenne Canyon, which she called a "great cathedral," instead of going to church. Over the course of her life, she traveled around the world, but no place touched her more deeply than the mountains of Colorado. Although she was in California at the time of her death, she requested that her body be buried in Colorado. She wanted her physical remains to rest in the same place where her heart and soul had found such lasting inspiration.

Courtesy, Colorado Historical Society F-33, 373

MRS. MAXWELL.

1

A Colorado Woman's Museum
First Published in St. Nicholas, *1876*
Original illustrations

You will ask yourselves, "What does that mean—a woman's museum?" and you will think, I suppose, that it means only a collection of curious things which some woman has bought and arranged in glass cases. Ah, it is quite different from that. I will try to tell you about it, and perhaps by the help of the pictures, and what I say, you will get some idea of how wonderful a museum it is.

There are many things in this museum—shells, minerals, coins, curious armor from Japan, queer garments from Alaska, tapa cloth from the Sandwich Islands, and a great many other curiosities, more than I can remember, or could have room in the ST. NICHOLAS to tell you about. I am going to tell you only about the stuffed animals and birds. These are the most interesting things in the museum, and the wonderful thing about them is, that they all were stuffed and many of them killed by the woman who owns the museum. Think of that!--of a woman's being able to fire her rifle as well as any old hunter could, and then, after she has brought down her bear or her wild-cat, knowing how to skin it and stuff it so that it looks exactly as if it were alive. This is really the most wonderful thing of all. You know very well how stuffed animals generally look. You know they are dead as far off as you can see them; but these animals all look as if they might walk off any minute they liked. Mrs. Maxwell (that is the name of the woman who has made this remarkable museum) is really a sculptor of animals. Most people who stuff animals, take the skin, I fancy, very much as a sausage-maker takes a sausage-skin, and simply cram into it as much as it will hold without bursting, for it is very elastic. I have heard that the skin of any animal will bear stretching till it is one-third larger than the animal was when alive. Well, if a dead animal's skin is as elastic as that, it is very easy to see how, in stuffing it, one might entirely spoil its shape and make it look unnatural. I have seen many a stuffed animal that didn't look any more like what it was when it was alive, than a sausage looks like a pig!

GROUP OF BIRDS, NO. 1.

Mrs. Maxwell stuffs her animals on a totally different plan, and this is why I say she is a sculptor of animals. The first thing she does is to mold the animal out of plaster, of the size and in the position she wishes. Then she fits the skin on the plaster shape. In the case of large animals, such as the bison or buffalo, she makes the figure partly of hay as well as of plaster, and what sort of a bison this results in you can see by the picture. I have never seen a live bison, but if I ever do, I do not believe he will put his head down and glare out from under his horns in one whit fiercer a way than this one does.

When I went into Mrs. Maxwell's museum, the first thing that caught my eye was a little black and tan terrier dog, lying under the table. He was a remarkably pretty dog, and, as we walked toward him, he fixed his eyes on us with a very keen and suspicious look, I thought. But he did not stir. I said to myself, "Why, what is the matter with that dog? Why doesn't he get up?" And then I saw that he was only a stuffed dog! Then I wished I had had a real live dog with me, to see if he wouldn't have been deceived too. I think he would.

Now I must tell you how the large groups of animals are arranged, for

GROUP OF BIRDS, NO. 2.

one reason that they look so natural is that Mrs. Maxwell has made an "outdoors" for them at one end of the room. She has had built up a sort of wooden frame-work, in the shape of rocks. This is covered with a coarse canvas cloth, which has been prepared with glue or some sticky substance. Over this, coarse shining sand of a dark gray color is sprinkled thick; and as the cloth is sticky, the sand remains. At a very little distance nobody would know the rocks from real rocks of dark gray stone. Then she has set real pine and fir trees among them, and little clumps of grasses, and mounds of real dirt. You can see all these in the pictures.

One of the most effective groups is the one where you see a large animal springing from a tree. That is a mountain

A GROUP OF ANIMALS.

lion. They are often found in the woods of Colorado. He is leaping down in the pursuit of the poor stag, which you see just to the right. The stag has run till he can run no longer; he is falling down on his knees, and his tongue is lolling out of his mouth, he is so out of breath. Just below these is a happy family of deer—father and mother and two little fawns. The little fawns are only a few days old. They are beautifully mottled with white spots on light brown. The doe is bending her neck down and licking one of them as affectionately as a cat licks her kitten, and father, just behind, is holding up his head and looking off very proudly, as much as to say, "Who's got a prettier family than I have, I'd like to know!"

Below them are some porcupines, muskrats, weasels, and small creatures; and off on the left, two splendid great bears, one a grizzly fellow that you wouldn't like to meet in the woods. Once, when I was riding in the woods on the rim of the Yosemite Valley, I saw the tracks of a grizzly bear in the sand. He had been there only a short time before us, for the tracks were very fresh. They looked just like the print of a giant's mittens, and they made us all feel very uncomfortable.

Another happy family in this museum is that of the mountain sheep—father, mother, and an only child. The father looks like a huge goat, with queer curling horns. The Colorado hunters see a great many like him, scrambling around on the rocks in high and precipitous places. Below him in the group is a fox, just ready to spring on a mouse, and near by is a wild-cat creeping out of a cave, and making up her mind to have a gray rabbit in front of her for dinner.

This group is not shown you, but you will have many a food laugh over those that the engraver has copied so

AN EXCITING GAME.

admirable. As I sit here in my Colorado home, it does my very heart good to think how many thousand children will shout over the pictures of the monkeys playing cards, and of the little house out of which Mr. Brown Squirrel and Miss Yellow Duckling are coming arm-in-arm to take a walk. Mrs. Maxwell calls this "The Moonlight Walk." The duckling is all covered with bright yellow down, and is not more than three or four inches high. I think she must have been caught as soon as she was fairly out of the shell. The squirrel is a head taller, as he ought to be, and has the most comical air of gallant protection toward his lady-love. They both look so droll, that nobody can help laughing at the first sight of them.

The monkeys, too, are very droll. One old fellow, with a pipe in his mouth, is scratching his head in his perplexity to know what card to play. The one next him is peering out from behind his cards, and watching the opposite monkey's face most keenly, to discover, if he can, what cards he holds;

and while they are all too absorbed in their game to see what is going on, a sly little rascal of a monkey is climbing up the leg of the table and taking their goblet.

But of all the groups, I am not sure that the prairie-dog's hole is not the very best. I see dozens of such mounds every day when I drive out, in Colorado, and on all the warm sunshiny days I see just such little prairie-dogs popping their heads out of the hole to find out who is going by, and there are always one or two more courageous ones who sit up on their haunches and look boldly at us. I have never happened to see either an owl or a rattlesnake on the mounds, but it is a well-known fact that they live in them. Mrs. Maxwell says she has often seen them come out of the holes, but "what their arrangements are for living there" she does not know, and nobody ever can know.

There would not be room here to tell you about half of the animals, neither can I tell you about the stuffed birds. They are as wonderful as the animals, and there are hundreds of them—all the birds of Colorado, and a great

THE PRAIRIE-DOG'S MOUND.

many of other countries. You will see by the two groups on the next page, however, that they look just as natural as the animals, and not at all like the usual double guidepost arrangements of stuffed birds. They look like flocks that had just alighted on a dead tree. You must not forget to look at the old mother-quail at the foot of one of these trees, with her little chickens all about her, one on her back and one sticking its head out through her wing. You'd think, if you called, "Chick, chick, chick," they'd all come running to get corn.

Now I can tell you about only two more things—an owl and a bird's nest. The owl is alive; it is Mrs. Maxwell's pet. She had two, but, unfortunately, her live bear ate up one of them. She found these young owls in their nest, when they were tiny little creatures, all covered with soft fluffy down. I saw them just after she found them, a year ago. They looked like little balls of gray feathers, with two big

"THE MOONLIGHT WALK."

glass beads sewed on them for eyes. Now, this little owl's downy feathers are all smooth and flat, and two small feather horns, looking just like cats' ears, have grown out of his head; and though he is only a few inches high, he looks as wise as any owl in the world. If you rub him gently on his head between his ears, he shuts his eyes right up and goes to sleep; but however sound asleep he seems to be, if you touch him on his back ever so lightly, he wakes up, makes a sharp angry noise, and whirls round and round quick as lightning, to bite your finger. Whenever he did this, he reminded me of a kitten going round and round after its tail. His head seems to be set on a pivot, for, without moving his body, he can turn it clear round, and see anything he wants to see behind him. He can also wink with one eye, while the other eye looks at you in a fixed stare. When he does this, his expression is more impudent than any human face could possibly wear. We laughed till the tears came into our eyes, watching this comical little creature.

I think that tears almost came into my eyes also when I looked at the bird's nest I am going to tell you of. They would not have been tears from laughter, however; they would have been tears of tender wonder and admiration for the little bird who built it.

Up in the mountains some thirty miles northwest of Denver is a wild canyon called Boulder Canyon. A canyon is a steep-sided valley between two mountains; sometimes it is little more than a rift between two precipices of rock. In this Boulder Canyon there is just room for a carriage-road and a swift little river, which is hardly more than a brook. Half-way down this canyon another canyon opens into it, and another swift little brook comes leaping sown

17

and fairly bounds into the first one. A few rods up this second canyon is a fine fall, or succession of falls, known as Boulder Falls. One day, a young man, sitting near these falls, saw a small bird fly apparently in the falling sheet of water. Presently it came back, was gone a short time, returned, bringing something in its beak, and second time darted into the spray and disappeared. This young man was an enthusiastic lover of natural history, and he determined to find out what that bird was doing behind Boulder Falls. If you only could see the place, you would wonder he ever had courage to venture where he did. He had to build a sort of bridge, and he had to wade in between rocks, where the stream was swift enough to knock him senseless in a very few minutes if he lost his footing; he really risked his life to track that little bird to her home. And do you not think he was rewarded when he found, snugly stowed away in a hollow behind the sheet of falling water, the nest, with the young birds in it?

Poor little bird! One would have thought she had found the very safest sort of a place which the whole world could offer; and so she had—safe against storm, against wild animals, against sportsmen, against everything except a naturalist!

The nest is made of clay and green moss; its mouth looks like the mouth of an old-fashioned brick oven; and there are all the little birds, with their mouths wide open, just as they waited for their mother to bring them food that day. The mother, too, he shot and brought away with the beautiful little house she had built. I think I could not have had the heart to kill her, even for the sake of the science of natural history. However, many things which seem cruel in themselves, must be done, or else we should never learn the truth about the wonderful creatures of which the world is full. But while I stood looking at the nest, I would have given a great deal to put it back under Boulder Falls again, with some happy little live birds in it, getting their dinner from their wet and dripping mamma. And the more I thought about it, the more I wondered whether it were really right for us ever to kill a living creature except for food. If there were a race of beings as much larger and stronger than we are, as we are than the birds, we would think it pretty hard, would we not, if they were in the habit of pulling our houses down over our heads, and killing us and our children, merely that they might classify us and label us and keep us in their museums?

THE BISON.

2

Ranch Life in Colorado
First Published in The Youth's Companion, *1880*

The word "ranch" is a contraction of the Spanish word "rancho," which means "a hut covered with branches or thatch for herdsmen," or "a farming establishment for the raising of horses and cattle."

In Colorado, and in California as well, the word has come to be applied indiscriminately to all farms, whether the land be used for grazing or for agricultural purposes. The word has a seductive sound. It suggests beautiful and picturesque surroundings, green trees, running streams, and a life of freedom and plenty; and I shall not soon forget the disappointment with which I first looked on a Colorado ranch.

A small, unpainted house, a story and a half high; a few outbuildings built of logs in the roughest manner; no fences; not a tree in sight; not a bush; chips and other litter all around; tin cans lying about in abundance; a most desolate-looking spot, with discomfort and deprivation staring you in the face at every point.

This was cattle ranch. The proprietor of it owned several thousand head of cattle.

He himself lived in a good house in Colorado Springs. This is the most comfortable way to keep a ranch; put a man, or men, in charge of it, and live yourself wherever you please, visiting the ranch often enough to see that things are in order. But, of course, this method is possible only to persons with means.

There are three sorts of ranches in Colorado: sheep ranches, cattle ranches, and farm ranches.

Cattle Ranches

The cattle interest is far the largest of the three. It is estimated that eight millions of money are invested in this business.

The principal grazing sections in the State are along the Platte, the Arkansas, and the Republican Rivers, but the plains in all sections are thus utilized.

Some of the Parks lying high up among the mountains also afford fine ranges. To the eye of a stranger, nothing could look more unsuited for grazing than the bare brown stretches of the Colorado plains.

But there is a sweetness and a nutrition in the low dried grasses which is wonderful. No hay that is made can compare with these grasses dried where they stand, and ready to be nibbled all winter.

Again, to a stranger, nothing could seem more improbable than that cattle should thrive, running all winter long unsheltered, uncared for, in a country where the mercury frequently falls at night to zero, and below, and where snow frequently covers the ground to several inches depth. But the facts show that cattle do thrive under these conditions.

They are very thin in the spring, and an exceptionally severe snow-storm in March or April will kill off some of the feeblest ones; but at the end of the year they make, on the whole, fair returns, and there are many cattle-men in the State who are growing steadily rich.

Sheep Ranches

The same is true of the sheep-men, though this business is subject to greater risks and fluctuations. When heavy snow-storms come, sheep are helpless; they are silly also, and sometimes in a single flock, hundreds will be stifled to death by their trampling each other under foot, in haste to get food which has been thrown down for them when they have been driven in after a long storm.

This last winter has been, in some parts of Colorado, exceptionally severe, and thousands of sheep have perished in the snow. The sheep-men have taken warning, and are putting up sheds on a large scale.

It would seem a simple matter of humanity, as well as policy, to provide them. Cattle can run before a storm, and will often, it is said, run forty miles to escape one; but the poor little sheep are too clumsy and slow; they are soon snowed in and under.

It is estimated that there are between five and six millions of dollars invested in the sheep business in the State, and Colorado wool is steadily growing in favor with manufacturers.

Farm Ranches

The agricultural interest in Colorado can never be a large one. It is a marvel that farmers will pass by the rich lands of Kansas to settle in a country where cold nights kill corn, and land must be irrigated to produce anything.
Wheat is the only grain crop on which it is worth while to count. Wheat does well. So do barley and oats; grass in valleys is abundant and good; and potatoes grow to a large size, and are excellent.

But the farmer has to work too hard. The trouble of making irrigating ditches and keeping up the supply of water is a serious addition to his labors. He will make at the best but a living, and that not a generous one.

To be content with this in a country where he sees men on all sides growing steadily rich by cattle or sheep, or making big fortunes in mines, a man must be either very lazy or very philosophical. In the ultimate future of Colorado, her industries and those of her neighboring States will, no doubt, be adjusted relatively to each other. She will make silver and gold, and they will send food to her.

Life on the larger and more remote ranches is lonely and monotonous to a degree which, it must be admitted, can hardly be wholesome for either mind or body.

The daily life of a herder of sheep, for instance, seems but one shade above that of the sheep themselves. He takes his flock out at daybreak, stands or lies still, watching them while they feed; drives them back to the ranch at night; cooks his own supper, washes the dishes, and goes to bed at nine o'clock, too tired to keep awake longer. This routine is varied by an interval of very hard work in the shearing season, and during the weeks when the lambs are born in the spring.

If ranch is near a town of size, he goes, perhaps once a week, to that town to buy what he needs; but the larger ranches are all remote from towns, and must necessarily be so, to secure sufficient range for large flocks and herds.

For a ranch sixty, seventy, or a hundred miles distant from its centre of supplies, purchases must be made by wholesale two or three times a year, and the ranchmen will have no intercourse with the world, except at these times, and when chance travellers pass by their place. A primitive and genuine hospitality is kept on most ranches; all travellers feel free to stop at them; and by no means the least of the fatigues of the ranchman's life is the preparing meals at any time for as many as happen to come.

These are some of the drawbacks on ranch life.

On the other hand, there are advantages by no means to be scorned; open air, year in and year out; freedom from all conventional and troublesome customs; independence, and the indefinable exhilaration, which almost all men find in a wild and untrammelled life.

The cattle-men for a great part of the year have little to do, except to keep their buildings in order, and attend to the few animals they keep with them. When the cattle are to be gathered together, branded and counted, or driven from one range to another, then the cattle-man rides, day after day, as madly as a Bedouin in the desert.

There is probably no better riding than can be seen at the summer "Round ups," as they are called, where dozens of vast herds of cattle have been gradually driven in from their ranges and collected in a dense mass in some open place, for the owners to pick out their respective cattle.

Any cow or steer found unbranded then can be taken possession of by anyone; such cattle are called *Mavericks* (for what reason, I cannot learn), and there are more of them than would be supposed; they might be called Ishmaelites among cattle.

As the ranchman prospers he adds building after building to his ranch. You may read the history of many ranches in the successive stages of building, from the roughest of log cabins, which was at first the dwelling, and is now merely and outhouse for tools, implements, etc., up to the two-story wooden house, possibly clapboarded, which the ranchman's wife takes pride, and in which you will find one or more carpeted rooms, a rocking-chair or two, and a newspaper or magazine.

I know one ranch, a sheep ranch, in which the record runs farther back than the log home; it runs back to a "dug out," a sort of compromise between a cave and a huge oblong ant-hill, in which the resolute sheep-man lived, or rather burrowed, for more than a year, when he began his Colorado life like David, with a "few sheep in the wilderness." Now he is the owner of two ranches, and many thousand sheep; but he has paid, by a permanently impaired digestion, the penalty for the months he spent in the "dug out," eating scanty and poor food.

The one chief and greatest objection to ranch life, as it is in Colorado at present, is the unwholesome food.

This need not be so bad, but there seems to be an unconquerable tendency in men living lonely and isolated lives, and doing with their own hands all the work to be done in the house, to shirk cooking, adopt the easiest methods, and fall into a dreary monotony of diet which is unwholesome.

The difficulty of procuring any variety of fresh meats, also, is another trouble which it is easier to evade by a perpetual recourse to ham and bacon than in any other way.

The trouble of milking cows and making butter is also very easily evaded by going without both butter and milk; and it is no uncommon thing to find a ranchman owning many hundreds of cows and not milking one. All of these things are to be taken account by invalids, who are often recommended, in a haphazard way, to "go out on some ranch and rough it for a year."

It would be a very exceptional invalid, or a very exceptional ranch, where there would not be more lost, by reason of bad food, than would be gained by the out-door life.

But after all is said and summed, for and against ranch life, there remains a certain element in it which can be neither said nor summed; and whose worth each individual will reckon at his own valuation, and cannot safely estimate for any other man. It is the nearness to nature, and the remoteness from man; all of which goes to make up his out-door life.

What the Bedouin knows of the desert, he could never tell; and the Colorado ranchman would probably find it quite as hard to give reasons for his love of ranch life.

3

Health Resorts in Colorado
First Published in The Youth's Companion, *1880*

The places in Colorado which come most properly under this head are Manitou, Cañon City, and Idaho Springs.

Manitou is by far the pleasantest of the three places I have named. It is a little hamlet nestled among the foothills at the base of Pike's Peak.

It is in the mouth of Ute Pass, which is one of the most beautiful short passes in the Rocky Mountains.

To reach Manitou, you go by the Denver and Rio Grande Railroad from Denver to Colorado Springs. Stages run from Colorado Springs to Manitou on the arrival of every train, and the distances is only about five miles.

There are two beautiful Cañons within easy walking distance from Manitou; through one of these a trail has been made leading up to the top of Pike's Peak.

The famous "Garden of the Gods," also, lies only about two miles away. The Fountain Creek, a pretty and swift little stream, runs through the centre of the village.

There are three large hotels and several boarding houses here, all of which in summer are crowed to overflowing with visitors. The advantages of Manitou for invalids are, that it is sheltered from winds, that it has pleasant and shady walks along the brook, that the hotels are better than the average hotels in Colorado, and that there are several sorts of medicinal water close at hand.

The disadvantages are that, owing to the high hills around it, the place gets in the winter an hour and a half less sunshine per day than the town of Colorado Springs, only five miles distant, that it is for the same reason sometimes hot and close in the summer, and is very dusty. There is now and then an invalid who finds the dampness from the brook objectionable; and all invalids find the throng of summer visitors wearisome and oppressive.

In July and August Manitou is like Newport or Saratoga, except that there is not so much fashion. A band plays every evening at the hotels, and that amusement known among Americans as "A Hop" occurs every week. Of course, under such circumstances no one can have the quite, the attention, or the food which an invalid needs.

Cañon City is not a city at all, but a small village lying at the mouth of the Grand Cañon of the Arkansas, about fifty miles southwest of Colorado Springs.

To reach it, you go by the Denver and Rio Grande Railroad from Denver to Pueblo; or can come from the East direct to Pueblo by the Atchison, Topeka and Santa Fe Railroad. At Pueblo, a branch of the Denver and Rio Grande Railroad runs to Cañon City.

The land is built on the banks of the Arkansas River, which comes out here from the "Grand Cañon," by which it has cut its way through the mountains.
This Cañon is one of the grandest sights in Colorado, and excursions to it are among the pleasantest features of life in Cañon City.

The town is dull and uninteresting; and the sandy cliffs, or buttes, to the back of it, are of a light drab color, which makes, under the hot Colorado sun, a glare almost as intolerable as that of white marble.

There is one very fair hotel there, and board can be had in a few of the private families.

The advantages of Cañon City for invalids are, that it is far enough to the South to be decidedly warmer in winter than either Manitou or Idaho; it is entirely sheltered from the north and northwest winds; the altitude is less, and the air is made moister by the nearness of the river, and therefore, for some invalids, much wholesomer, being less electric and exciting. There are pleasant drives and excursions into the near mountain; and for botanists, the flora of the region is of itself an occupation.

The disadvantages are that it is very hot in summer, and very dull at times; and the immediate views are not beautiful and interesting, like those at Manitou. The river water, also, which is the water drunk in the town, is often muddy and disagreeable.

Idaho is a little village in the mountains, a half day's journey by rail and stage northwest from Denver.

To reach it, you go by the Colorado Central Railroad, three or four hours from Denver, through the celebrated Clear Creek Cañon, which contains some of the grandest scenery in the State. The village is surrounded by hills, and there is a little brook running through it, as at Manitou, but owing to the greater altitude and poorer soil, there is much less foliage; and the place never looks so green and attractive as Manitou.

There is one good hotel and, connected with it, several cottages which are occupied by visitors. In summer the place is crowded with people, largely people from Denver seeking a refuge from the intolerable heat of that sun-smitten city.

There are very complete arrangements for baths at Idaho, much more so than at Cañon City or Manitou. The temperature of the water ranges from 70° to 110° Fahrenheit, and it is very largely impregnated with soda.

The advantages of Idaho are its sheltered situation, making it much warmer in the winter than most places which are so high; the vicinity of grand scenery and mining regions of great interest; and a hotel much better than the average Colorado hotel.

The disadvantages are the altitude (eight thousand feet), which is too great for many patients, the extreme quiet and dulness of the place in winter, and its dust in summer.

There are several other points in Colorado at which mineral springs are found, and to which invalids have found their way; Morrison Springs, at Morrison, twelve miles west of Denver, on the Denver and South Park Railroad; the Hot Sulphur Springs in Middle Park and in South Park; the Cottonwood Hot Springs, on the Cottonwood branch of the Arkansas River, ninety miles west of the town of Colorado Springs, and the Poncho Hot Springs, situated in the Poncho Pass, in Lake County,—all these are sulphur springs, some hot and some cold; in none of these places, however, have arrangements yet been made at all complete or comfortable for the accommodation of invalids.

Of the other places in Colorado suitable for invalids seeking simply the climate influences, and not wishing to drink or bathe in medicinal waters, the city of Denver and the town of Colorado Springs are the chief. The merits of these two places are so warmly upheld by their respective advocates that it is almost dangerous to discuss them in either place, and perhaps well-nigh impossible for a person who likes one to do justice to the other. Certainly no one ever liked both.

Denver is a city with some twenty thousand inhabitants. Colorado Springs is a village (called a city), with not more than four thousand. Denver has big hotels, big shops, sidewalks (chiefly wooden), a theatre, concert-halls, billiard-rooms. Colorado Springs has two or three small hotels (as poor as Denver's big ones), a few small shops, grass-bordered paths, one town-hall, one billiard-room, and no whiskey-saloon.

Denver is rich; there are plenty of people there who have made big fortunes, built big house, and keep fast horses. A certain unenlightened extravagance is very noticeable. Showy clothes and ostentatious entertainment are common.

The expression of the city and its people would strike any Eastern traveller, walking up and down its streets for a few days, as being crude, fast, and flashy, redeemed to a degree by evident activity, energy, success, and a disposition to do everything in a liberal, and so far as things are understood, elegant manner. It has, in short, all the faults, foibles, and excellencies of a new rich Western city.

Colorado Springs is not rich. There is not in the town a man who would be called rich in New York. There are no big houses; there is no fast living; its ways are country ways; showy clothes and ostentatious entertainment would be ridiculous.

The whole expression of the town strikes travellers from the Eastern States as being like that of a New England village; small, neatly kept, comfortable homes; and the two biggest buildings in town are a Deaf and Dumb Asylum and a stone schoolhouse; a handsome college building, which is fast going up, also of stone, will, when it is completed, add still more to the New England look of the town.

In the matter of climate there is, perhaps, not so much difference between the two places as their respective advocates claim, but to hear the assertions on both sides, one would think that either one or the other place must prove fatal to most invalids.

Denver is a few hundred feet lower than the Springs; this is for many invalids a gain. Denver is colder in winter, and hotter in summer; it lies open and unsheltered on the plains; the mountains thirty miles away. Colorado Springs lies close to the base of the Pike's Peak range, sheltered by the Divide, a table-land eight thousand feet high, from winds from the north.

In the matter of scenery, immediately surrounding, or easily accessible, it would seem that there could be no claim set up for Denver, in comparison with Colorado Springs.

Yet there are those who assert that the one grand view of the main range, which is, no doubt, simply superb from Denver, more than outweighs all the picturesque beauty of the surroundings of the Springs. But to a true lover of nature, no one single view, however grand and however varied by changing atmospheric effects, can be so sufficing and so inexhaustible in pleasure as a region full of beautiful views, streams, woods, ravines, and climbable mountains, such as are to be enjoyed in the near neighborhood of Colorado Springs.

There are ten beautiful Cañons within an easy day's excursion from the town; most of them within reach by an afternoon's drive. There is the famous "Garden of the Gods," and "Monument Park," there is Cheyenne

Mountain, with its numerous promontory-like spurs, covered with grand pines, into the shade of which one can drive in an hour and a half from the town.

The relief, the blessing of this, after a scorching day of Colorado sunshine, cannot be told, neither is it possible to put in words the perpetual blessing to a lover of mountains of their near presence, friendliness, and shelter.

The elements of choice for invalids between Denver and Colorado Springs as a place of sojourn are easily summed up

The person who is accustomed to city routines, to depending upon people who like noise and movement, and has not learned to find occupation and delight in out-door life, would far better stay in Denver. He will be bored at Colorado Springs, and not know what to do with himself there.

The person who likes quiet, has resources within himself, is content with only a moderate and informal social life, and loves to drive, ride, and ramble in wild places, who can spend whole days happily with a friend, a book, a pine-tree, and the sky over his head, would better come straight to Colorado Springs. He will be bored and irritated in Denver, and not know what to do with himself there.

4

Health-Seeking in Colorado
First Published in The Youth's Companion, *1880*

"All that a man hath will he give for his life," is as true now as it was in the days of Job, and one of the saddest spectacles which the earth affords today is the melancholy caravan of invalids journeying hither or thither in search of a man, or an air, that can prolong their days a little.

Within the last few years Colorado has come much into notice as a place of resort for invalids, chiefly for invalids suffering from asthma or consumption. Rash and unfounded generalizations have been widely scattered by newspaper correspondents; the numbers of cures have been exaggerated; the advantages of the climate have been over-stated. Its disadvantages have not been mentioned. For these reasons there is today a steady influx into the State of men and women who are leaving comfortable homes in the East, sacrificing assured incomes from professions or trades, and exposing themselves to all sorts of hardships and deprivations under the belief or hope that "Colorado will cure" them.

It is plain that there must be a genuine and substantial cause for such a movement as this; but it would save disappointment to vast numbers of people if it were generally and accurately known just what is, and what is not, to be expected from the Colorado climate; just what can be, and what cannot be done in Colorado; and so far as is possible by general statements, what course an invalid coming here had better pursue.

The Climate of Colorado

For the benefit, then, of persons who from sickness are under the necessity of seeking a change of climate, let me try to answer the question, what is, and what is not, to be expected from the Colorado climate.

It is not specifically curative. It is not a medicine. It can often arrest consumption, in the earlier stages of that disease, simply because the air is so dry that the lung tissues cannot go on altering. Ulcers on internal surfaces dry up, just as the external skin dries up when deprived of moisture. Owing to this, the disease is arrested; nature has a chance to attend to her own instinctive healing; the patient is better; gains strength; feels himself saved.

Often after this result is secured the patient goes back East. Of course, he breaks down again in a few months with the same or with worse trouble, and then it is said that Colorado did not do him any real good after all.

The trouble was not with Colorado, but the man and his friends had expected too much. He might have lived to a good old age in Colorado. While he was there his disease was like an enemy whose weapons were taken away, and whose hands were tied. Going back to the lower attitude and moister air, he freed his enemy and put the weapons into his hands again.

Asthma and Consumption

In the case of asthma, which is the only disease of which it is safe to say that it is nearly always relieved in Colorado, what I have said about a change of climate is also true.

The asthmatic patient breathes here with ease. He says, "I am well." So long as he stays in Colorado, Colorado will compel his lungs to do him good service, but she gives no guaranteed passports to asthmatics to go beyond her lines. In the cases of more advanced consumption, there is, of course, less benefit to be expected from the climate of Colorado. Still there are many persons living here in fairly comfortable health, able to do some work, who have very serious organic disease. They will probably die of consumption in Colorado, but it will be several years later than they would have died in the East.

Debility

Perhaps the invalids, next to the asthmatics, who are surest to be helped here in Colorado are those suffering from general debility and prostration.

There is a marvellous tonic in the dry air and in the sunshine. But to reap this benefit the weakened patients must lead out-door lives, and obey strictly all the laws of health, which in nine cases out of ten they have been in the habit of breaking at home.

And this brings me to the head of what can and cannot be done in Colorado.

Inconveniencies

What inconveniences and drawbacks must a patient encounter in Colorado? An invalid cannot get the food he ought to have, unless he keeps house. The hotels and boarding-houses are, as a rule, poor.

This is not for lack of good food in the markets; it is owing to the fact that the standard of cooking in Colorado is low.

Opportunities of Employment

If the invalid needs to support himself, he will find it a hard thing to do. The country is new. The higher needs of society are yet not much recognized, and the lower are amply met.

A delicate and fastidious man or woman--and consumptives are almost always both--needing to earn money in Colorado, is at a sore disadvantage. For one situation for a teacher or minister, for one chance of earning money by painting, giving lessons, sewing, singing, or writing, there are scores of persons who are seeking such employments.

A man who can dig in a mine, work in a carpenter's shop; a woman can (or will) take a situation as house servant here,—can command work and earn very high wages. Few others can. I get letters every month asking if there is any way for an invalid to earn a living here, —to earn even his board; and I have but one reply to make, that Colorado is a very hard country in every way for a person without means. A few of the bare necessaries of life--beef, flour, coal--are cheap. Everything that can be called a luxury is dear. Muscle is in demand; money is in demand; brain-work and accomplishments are not.

If the invalid needs amusements, if he is a person without internal resources, accustomed to depend on the excitements and pleasures of city life, he will be badly off in Colorado. Nothing but a strong love of nature, and a firmly fixed habit of being happy in a quiet life, can make a person contented in Colorado.

What Can a Patient Do?

Now let me tell you what the invalid can do. He can spend more days in the open air in the course of a calendar year than he can in any climate in the world, unless it be that of Madeira. He can ride; he can drive; he can live in a tent; he can botanize in one of the most interesting floras in the world; he can geologize in a field full of perplexing interest; he can study human nature in new and varied aspects. If he is strong enough, and has the pecuniary means, he can visit the mining towns, and can see there phases of life which he can nowhere except in mining districts. He can climb mountains fourteen thousand feet high; he can explore canyons twelve hundred deep.

If he has capital at command, he can invest some of it in sheep or cattle; and either put them under the care of a competent man, or take charge of them himself.

He can live in a small shanty, and do his own cooking; and if he has sufficient pluck and sense of humor to enjoy the situation, he will gain more, perhaps, in that way of life than in any other.

He can buy a camping outfit, and travel for four or five months in the year, sleeping in a tent every night. If he likes this, it will do him good. If he hates it, it will do him harm.

Who Should not go to Colorado

There is one thing that is not generally known, but which ought to be by all persons who think of coming to Colorado. It is the effect of the rarefied air upon the action of the heart. The pulse-beat is from ten to twelve per minute quicker here than at the sea-level.

This stimulus to circulation, while it is in many cases one

of the beneficial agencies in the Colorado air, is in other cases very injurious. Persons with any form of heart-disease, or with any tendency to it, should never come here.

The electric conditions are also very peculiar, and as yet little understood. Some nervous persons are unable to sleep, and are obliged to go away in consequence.

The severe wind-storms which prevail in March and April, and occur occasionally in all other parts of the year, have a very seriously disturbing influence upon many people, causing in some great sleeplessness and a vague but intolerable discomfort; causing in others unconquerable drowsiness, so that they are obliged to go to sleep even in the middle of the day, as soon as the winds begin to blow. It is, of course, impossible in a short an article as this to give any minute details of Colorado life, or to give more than the briefest suggestions as to the effects of the climate. But I think I have said enough to partially give the information needed by many who are thinking of seeking a temporary home here.

I cannot better sum up the results of my own five years' observation and experience here than by saying, firstly, that I regard a trial of this climate as purely experimental in each individual case; secondly, that I never see a suffering invalid at the East without wishing he could have the opportunity to make that experiment.

5

The Ants' Monday Dinner

First Published in Bits of Talk, *1876*

How did I know what the ants had for dinner last Monday? Ha, it is odd that I should have known, but I'll tell you how it happened.

I was sitting under a big pine-tree, high up on a high hill-side. The hill-side was more than seven thousand feet above the sea, and that is higher than many mountains which people travel hundreds of miles to look at. But this hill-side was in Colorado, so there was nothing wonderful in being so high up. I had been watching the great mountains with snow on them, and the great forests of pine-trees—miles and miles of them—-so close together that it looks as if you could lie down on their tops and not fall through; and my eyes were tired with looking at such great, grand things, so many miles off; so I looked down on the ground where I was sitting, and watched the ants which were running about everywhere, as busy and restless as if they had the whole world on their shoulders.

Suddenly I saw, under a tuft of grass, a tiny yellow caterpillar, which seemed to be bounding along in a very strange way. In a second more, I saw an ant seize hold of him and begin to drag him off. The caterpillar was three times as long as the ant, and his body was more than twice as large round as the biggest part of the ant's body.

"Ho! ho! Mr. Ant," said I, "you needn't think you're going to be strong enough to drag that fellow very far."

Why, it was about the same thing as if you or I should drag off a heifer, which was kicking and struggling for dear life all the time; only that the heifer hasn't half so many legs to catch hold of things with as the caterpillar had. Poor caterpillar! how he did try to get away! But the ant never gave him a second's time to take a good grip of anything; and he was cunning enough, too, to drag him on his side, so that he couldn't use his legs very well. Up and down, and under and over stones and sticks; in and out of tufts of grass; up to the very top of the tallest blades, and then down again; over gravel and sand, and across bridges of pine-needles from stone to stone; backward all the way—but for all I could see, just as swiftly as if he were going headforemost—ran that ant, dragging the caterpillar after him. I watched him very closely, thinking, of course, he must be making for his house. Presently, he darted up the trunk of the pine-tree.

"Dear me!" said I, "ants don't live in trees! What does this mean?"

The bark of the tree was all broken and jagged, and full of seams twenty times as deep as the height of the ant's body. But he didn't mind; down one side and up the other he went. They must have been awful chasms to him; and to the poor caterpillar too, for their sharp edges caught and tore his skin, and doubled him up a dozen ways in a minute. And yet the ant never once stopped or went a bit slower. I had to watch very closely, not to lose sight of him altogether. I began to think that he was merely trying to kill the caterpillar; that, perhaps, he didn't mean to eat him, after all. Perhaps he was merely a gentlemanly sportsman ant, out on a frolic. How did I know but some ants might hunt caterpillars, just as some men hunt deer, for fun, and not at all because they need food? If I had been sure of this, I would have spoiled Mr. Ant's sport for him very soon, you may be sure, and set the poor caterpillar free. But I never heard of an ant's being cruel; and if it were really for dinner for his family that he was working so hard, I thought he ought to be helped, and not hindered. Just then my attention was diverted from him by a sharp cry overhead. I looked up, and there was an enormous hawk, sailing round in circles, with two small birds flying after him, pouncing down on his head, and then darting away, and all the time making shrill cries of fright and hatred. I knew very well what that meant. Mr. Hawk was also out trying to do some marketing for his dinner; and he had his eye on some little birds in their nest; and there were the father and mother birds driving him away. You wouldn't have believed two such little birds could have driven off such a big creature as the hawk, but they did. They seemed to fairly buzz round his head as flies do round a horse's head, and at last he just gave up and flew off so far that he vanished in the blue sky, and the little birds came skimming home again into the wood.

"Well, well," said I, "the little people are stronger than the big ones, after all! Where has my ant gone?"

Sure enough! It hadn't been two minutes that I had been watching the hawk and the birds, but in that two minutes the ant and the caterpillar had disappeared. At last I found them, — where do you think? In a fold of my water-proof cloak, on which I was sitting! The ant had let go of the caterpillar, and was running round and round him, perfectly bewildered; and the caterpillar was too near dead to stir. I shook the fold out, and as soon as the cloth lay straight and smooth, the ant fastened his nippers in the caterpillar again, and started off as fast as ever. I suppose if I could have seen his face, and had understood the language of ants' features, I should have seen plainly written there, "Dear me, what sort of a country was that I tumbled into, so frightfully black and smooth?" By this time the caterpillar had had the breath pretty well knocked out of his body, and was so limp and helpless that the ant was not afraid of his getting away from him. So he stopped a second now and then to rest. Sometimes he would spring on the caterpillar's back, and stretch himself out there; sometimes he would stand still on one side and look at him sharply, keeping on nipper on his head. All the time, though, he was working steadily in one direction; he was headed for home now, I felt very certain. It astonished me very much at first, that none of the ants he met took any notice of him; they all went on their own way, and never took so much as a sniff at the caterpillar. But pretty soon I said to myself, "You stupid woman, not to suppose that ants can be as well behaved as people! When you passed Mr. Jones yesterday, you didn't peep into his market-basket, nor touch the big cabbage he had under his arms."

Presently, the ant dropped the caterpillar, and ran on a few steps—I mean inches—to meet another ant who was coming towards him. They put their heads close together for a second. I could not hear what they said, but I could easily imagine, for they both ran quickly back to the caterpillar, and one took him by the head and the other by the tail, and then they lugged him along finely. It was only a few steps, however, to the ant's house; that was the reason he happened to meet this friend just coming out. The door was a round hole in the ground, about as big as my little finger. Several ants were standing in the door-way, watching

46

these two come up with the caterpillar. They all took hold as soon as the caterpillar was on the door-step, and almost before I knew he was fairly there, they had tumbled him down, heels over head, into the ground, and that was the last I saw of him.

The oddest thing was how the ants came running home from all directions. I don't believe there was any dinner-bell rung, though there might have been one too fine for my ears to hear; but in less than a minute, I had counted thirty-three ants running down that hole. I fancied they looked as hungry as wolves.

I had a great mind to dig down into the hole with a stick, and see what had become of the caterpillar. But I thought it wasn't quite fair to take the roof off a man's house to find out how he cooks his beef for dinner; so I sat still awhile, and wondered whether they would lay him straight on the floor, and all stand in rows each side of him and nibble across, and whether they would leave any for Tuesday; and then I went home to my own dinner.

6

Colorado Snow-Birds

First Published in St. Nicholas, *1875*
Original illustration

I'll tell you how the snow-birds come,
    Here in our Winter days;
They make me think of chickens,
    With their cunning little ways.

We go to bed at night, and leave
    The ground all bare and brown,
And not a single snow-bird
    To be seen in all the town.

But when we wake at morning
    The ground with snow is white,
And with the snow, the snow-birds
    Must have traveled all the night;

For the streets and yards are full of them,
    The dainty little things,
With snow-white breasts, and soft brown heads
    And speckled russet wings.

Not here and there a snow-bird,
    As we see them at the East,
But in great flocks, like grasshoppers,
    By hundreds, at the least.

They push and crowd and jostle,
    And twitter as they feed,
And hardly lift their heads up
    For fear to miss a seed.

What 't is they eat, nobody seems
    To know or understand;
The seeds are much too fine to see,
    All sifted in the sand.

But winds last Summer scattered them,
    All thickly on these plains;
The little snow-birds have no barns,
    But God protects their grains.

They let us come quite near them,
    And show no sign of dread;
Then, in a twinkling, the whole flock
    Will flutter on ahead

A step or two, and light, and feed,
    And look demure and tame,
And then fly again, and stop,
    As if it were a game.

Some flocks count up to thousands,
    I know, and when they fly,
Their tiny wings make rustle,
    As if a wind went by.

They go as quickly as they come,
  Go in a night or day;
Soon as the snow has melted off,
  The darlings fly away,

But come again, again, again,
  All Winter, with each snow;
Brave little armies, through the cold,
  Swift back and forth they go.

I always wondered where they lived
  In Summer, till last year
I stumbled on them in their home,
  High in the upper air;

'Way up among the clouds it was,
  A many thousand feet,
But on the mountain-side gay flowers
  Were blooming fresh and sweet.

Great pine-trees' swaying branches
  Gave cool and fragrant shade;
And here, we found, the snow-birds
  Their Summer home had made.

"Oh, ye lucky little snow-birds,"
  We said, "to know so well,
In Summer time and Winter time,
  Your destined place to dwell—

"To journey, nothing doubting,
  Down to the barren plains.
Where harvests are all over,
  To find your garnered grains!

"Oh, precious little snow-birds,
  If we were half as wise,
If we were half as trusting
  To the Father in the skies—

"He would feed us, though the harvests
  Had ceased throughout the land,
And hold us, all our lifetime,
  In the hollow of His hand!"

Cited Works
by Helen Hunt Jackson

"The Ants' Monday Dinner." *Bits of Talk, in Verse and Prose, for Young Folks*. Boston: Roberts Brothers, 1876.

Bits of Travel at Home. Boston: Roberts Brothers, 1878.

A Century of Dishonor: A Sketch of the United States Government's Dealings with Some of the Indian Tribes. New York: Harper, 1881.

"Colorado Snow-Birds." *St. Nicholas*, April 1875: 330–331.

"A Colorado Woman's Museum." *St. Nicholas*, October 1876: 781–784.

"Health Resorts in Colorado." *The Youth's Companion*, 13 May 1880: 165–166.

"Health-Seeking in Colorado." *The Youth's Companion*, 6 May 1880: 153–154.

Nelly's Silver Mine: A Story of Colorado Life. Boston: Roberts Brothers, 1878.

Ramona. Boston: Roberts Brothers, 1884.

"Ranch Life in Colorado." *The Youth's Companion*, 20 May 1880: 173–174.

Secondary Sources

Banning, Evelyn I. *Helen Hunt Jackson*. New York: Vanguard, 1973.

Benson, Maxine. *Martha Maxwell: Rocky Mountain Naturalist*. Lincoln: University of Nebraska Press, 1986.

Mathes, Valerie Sherer. *Helen Hunt Jackson and Her Indian Reform Legacy*. Austin: University of Texas Press, 1990.

Odell, Ruth. *Helen Hunt Jackson*. New York: D. Appleton-Century Co., 1939.

West, Mark I., ed. *Westward to a High Mountain: The Colorado Writings of Helen Hunt Jackson*. Denver: Colorado Historical Society, 1994.